TALES IN PRAISE OF THE ARI

TALES IN PRAISE OF THE ARI

ספר
שבחי האר"י ז"ל
ומעשה נסים

אין לאדינו דחונדו אם חינטינדיר לם
מעלת די חיל רב החר"י ז"ל קון סוס
תלמידי"חי מעשיות קי חקונטיסיירון
אין סו טיינפו · חי מילרחגרופי דיטה
לינ"רו סירה זוכה לחיי העולם הבא ·

לו טרושיו אלה איסטאנפה ח'
חיים אליה פ'ארדו הי"ו: אילקי
וינדי ליברוס אין יני חאן

נדפס
בקושטאנדינה

אשר תחת ממצלת אדוננו המלך פולטן
מוסטאפה יר"ח

סנת התקכ"ו

TALES

in Praise of the ARI

Translated from the Hebrew by Aaron Klein
and Jenny Machlowitz Klein

Solomon Shelemiel ben Hayyim

Drawings by
MOSHE RAVIV

The Jewish Publication Society of America
Philadelphia, Pa., 1970 – תש"ל

COPYRIGHT © 1970

BY THE JEWISH PUBLICATION SOCIETY OF AMERICA

FIRST EDITION / ALL RIGHTS RESERVED

LIBRARY OF CONGRESS CATALOG CARD NUMBER: 76-105064 ✓

MANUFACTURED IN THE UNITED STATES OF AMERICA

DESIGNED BY ISMAR DAVID

TALES in Praise of the ARI

THERE once lived a man in Israel, the glorious land, and his name was Rabbi Solomon, of blessed memory. And this man was whole-hearted and upright and God-fearing and one who shunned evil. Now it came to pass one day, as he was in the synagogue studying by himself, that Elijah the Prophet—may he be remembered for good—appeared to him, saying: "Know that I am a messenger of God and I come to bring you tidings that your wife will conceive and bear you a son, and you shall call him Isaac. And he will set about to deliver Israel from evil spirits and through him many souls, now in a transformed state, will be brought to their perfection. He will reveal the hidden mysteries of the Torah and the meaning of the Zohar, and his fame will go forth throughout the world. Therefore take special heed that you do not circumcise him till I myself come and be the child's godfather."

And it came to pass that when he finished speaking he disappeared, and Rabbi Solomon remained all that day in the synagogue, weeping and praying to God. And thus he spoke: "Master of the universe, fulfill the good tidings that You have brought me. And though I am not worthy, do it for Your sake and not for mine. And do not let my sins cause these good tidings to be of no effect." That night he went home but he did not reveal this matter even to his wife. And Solomon knew his wife and she conceived and bore a son, and the whole house was filled with light and the man rejoiced in his offspring.

On the eighth day he brought him to the synagogue to be circumcised according to the custom. The father looked around all the four corners of the synagogue to see whether Elijah, of blessed memory, had come as he had said he would. But he saw him not. And all who were present urged him, saying: "Come, take your son and circumcise him." He answered that not all of his relatives had yet come. When about an hour had passed and Elijah had not appeared, the father thought in the bitterness of his soul: If Elijah has not appeared, it can only be because of my sins. And even as he wept, behold, Elijah appeared to him, saying: "Refrain from weeping, O servant of the Lord. Approach the altar and prepare your sacrifice. Take my seat and I myself will circumcise the child. For I did but tarry to know whether you would keep my commandments and hearken unto me."

Then Elijah took the child from the woman and circumcised him, but no one saw him save the father. And as soon as the child arrived home, he was healed as though he had been circumcised many years before. And the child grew and was weaned and was brought to school, and at once learned more than any child of his age. At five, he studied the Bible and the Mishnah. At eight, he was learning the Talmud with penetrating diligence.

At this time, his father died. After the days of mourning, his mother said to him: "You surely are aware that I am now a widow and am unable to buy books for you as is meet. Therefore, I pray that you hearken unto me. Let us arise and go to your uncle in Egypt. There you will lack for nothing." And Isaac said: "Here am I." They then arose and went down to Egypt where his uncle welcomed him warmly and urged Rabbi Bezalel Ashkenazi to accept him as a pupil. So it came to pass that he taught him and found him clear in understanding. After two years, his knowledge surpassed that of all the rabbis of Egypt and no scholar could equal him in the force of his discussion.

His uncle then gave him his daughter in marriage and showed him great honor, and gave him a rich dowry.

ONE day, as he sat praying in the synagogue, a man sat next to him. The rabbi turned and saw a book in his hand in which he beheld heavenly mysteries. After the prayer, the rabbi said to the man: "Tell me what is written in this book." The man answered, saying: "What shall I say, inasmuch as the Lord hath withheld honor from me. For I am of the Marranos. Seeing that everyone prayed from a book, in my embarrassment, I also took a book, but I know not what is written therein." Said the rabbi to him: "In that case, sell me this book and I will give you a prayer book." He then said: "Do I lack money that I should sell you this book? Rather ask your father-in-law to remit the taxes on my merchandise and I will give you the book." As the rabbi was eager for the book, he entreated his father-in-law, who agreed to his request and obtained the book for him.

The rabbi studied this book and the Book of Splendor—the Zohar—with all his might while he fasted and afflicted himself. Through these acts he merited that in dreams at night he would sometimes be told that his understanding of a passage of the Zohar was not correct. Again, at other times, he would be told that he understood correctly, but not in accordance with the meaning of Rabbi Simeon bar Johai. At long last he was told that if he truly desired to understand the text, he must increase his self-affliction. This he did.

And when he saw that he was on the right path, he retired to the Nile region in Egypt for six years, and in holiness and purity occupied himself with study day and night. Thereby he merited that each night his soul was raised up and asked to which heavenly academy it wished to ascend—to the academy of Rabbi Eliezer the Great, or the academy of Rabbi Akiba, or to that of Rabbi Simeon bar Johai. And withersoever his soul desired, there it was taken and awesome mysteries were revealed to it. When morning came he had not forgotten anything and would reveal all to his disciples.

ONE time, a Hasid, Rabbi Abraham Halevi, found the Ari asleep and his lips moving. Coming near him, Rabbi Abraham Halevi drew his ear close to the mouth of Rabbi Isaac, of blessed memory, to hear what he was saying. At this moment, the rabbi awoke from his slumber and saw Rabbi Abraham standing over him. He asked him: "What are you doing here?" Rabbi Abraham replied: "Forgive me, O Master; I saw you, O glory of the Torah, asleep with lips aflutter and I put my ear close to hear what my Master was saying." The Ari, of blessed memory, answered: "Always when I sleep, my soul ascends to heaven by divers paths known unto me, and the ministering angels come forth to meet me and welcome my soul and bring me before Metatron, Prince of the Divine Presence, who asks me to which academy I desire to go. In these academies are revealed to me the secrets and mysteries of the

8

Torah which were neither heard nor known even in the days of the *tanaaim*, on whom be peace." Said Rabbi Abraham: "Will not my Master reveal to me what they taught him this time?" The Master, on whom be peace, laughed and said: "I call heaven and earth to witness that were I to talk for eighty consecutive years, it is no exaggeration that I would not be able to complete what I learned this time on the portion concerning Balaam and the ass."

All this he merited after he came up from Egypt to the Holy Land.

ONCE the men of Safed appointed ten wise and sage men, the Ari, of blessed memory, being included among them, to be the wards over moral conduct. One day one of these men rose up early to go to the synagogue to be among the first ten men, as was his custom. On opening the window to see whether the dawn had come, he saw a bedizened woman leaving her house. The official followed her and saw her enter a house occupied by a man suspected of immoral relations with women. The official thereupon said: "Truly the thing is now known that this woman is a wanton." He therefore set men to prevent them from sinning. He went at once to the synagogue and instructed the beadle to assemble all the wardens after prayer. When they were assembled, he arose to testify concerning what he had seen that morning. But even before he could utter a word, the Master called out to him: "Hold your tongue, and do not speak evil against a blameless woman of Israel. For this woman whom you saw is entirely without sin. She went early so that none would see her. For to this selfsame house had come a man from the West to bring from her husband a letter and a sum of money. She had asked him to send her this sum, but he replied that her husband had entrusted to him a secret to be revealed to her and her alone, and not to turn it over to a messenger. Therefore she herself had gone to meet him." And when the ward heard this, he remained silent and instead went to investigate further into this matter. Finding that the Master was justified, he came to him and pleaded: "I entreat you to forgive me." The Master replied: "You have done nothing against me. Rather go to the woman and beg forgiveness from her for your suspicion." He did so. Thereafter the Master was regarded as a prophet.

Nevertheless, two learned men placed no credence in him. One day they came to test him. They found him out of doors and said to him: "Are you the seer who knows what a person has done during his lifetime?" With great modesty he denied this and replied: "I am neither a prophet nor the son of a prophet." And even as he spoke, a man passed by and touched the Master's garment. And he said: "May the Lord forgive you for you have made it necessary for me to perform many ablutions because of you." When the learned men heard these words, they hurried after the man and said: "Please tell us what you did that the Master spoke thus unto you. Tell us and we will accompany you to the Master and intercede for you that He prescribe for you a penance lest you die unchastened." The man was much affrighted and said: "What can I say and

נ"ג
Raviv '65

how justify myself, seeing that God has disclosed the sin of your humble servant. For this night I was drunk and the serpent enticed me to lie with my wife in an unnatural manner." When the learned men heard this, they marveled and went with this man to the Master and pleaded with Him to prescribe for him an act of penance. He granted their request and thereafter they never forsook the person of the Master.

NOW notwithstanding all these accomplishments of the Ari, Rabbi Hayim Vital sojourned in Damascus. Every night the Master would remove Rabbi Hayim's soul from its earthly garb and hold discourse with him. In the morning Rabbi Hayim would relate this to his disciples, saying: "There is a learned Ashkenazi in Safed and each night he holds discourse with my soul and urges me to come to him that he may teach me the Torah." And since in his own view he held himself to be wiser than the Master, he spoke almost with scorn; the more so seeing that he had already written a commentary on the Zohar. One day he found difficulty with a passage, and though he labored over it diligently he yet failed to grasp the meaning. Still another day, he found difficulty with a second passage; and again with a third—none of which he could understand.

Seeing how matters stood, he said: "Let me go to visit Safed, and while there I will see whether the Master is indeed equal to his repute." And on the day he came to Safed, he went to the Master who received him warmly and accorded him honor. Rabbi Hayim Vital put to him the first difficult passage, and he explained it clearly. He consulted him regarding the second passage, and the Master opened wide to him the gates of illumination. When it came to the third passage, the Master said: "This is the limit of your understanding. You are not worthy to delve further." Rabbi Hayim was as a fox who stands before the lion. Crestfallen, he left him, came to his house, took off his garments and clothed himself in sackcloth and sat all that day and fasted, weeping and praying to the Lord that he might find grace and favor in the eyes of the Master, so that he would accept him as a disciple.

The next morning he returned to the Master and implored him to take him as a disciple. Then the Master replied: "By right I should not accept you because you tarried these three months before coming to me. But your act of penance yesterday has been in your favor so that I shall accept you and not hide anything from you." Whereat Rabbi Hayim prostrated himself before the Ari and cried out: "May the King live forever." He sat and studied together with the other scholars. However, he would always forget what he had learned until one day the Master went with his disciples to Tiberias and had him drink water from the well of Miriam. Thenceforth he retained whatever he would learn.

IT happened one day as they were studying that the Master turned and saw in a tree

two ravens with plucked feathers. He called out to them: "Evil ones! In this world you sought to destroy an entire people and now in your distress you turn to me. Get you hence!" They fled in haste. The disciples then asked: "What is the meaning of this?" He replied: "Know that these ravens are Balak and Balaam who were taken from one hell, Gehinnam, to be placed in a more terrible hell. They came to beg of me forgiveness for the humiliation that had been put upon me, and that I pray in their behalf that they be saved from hell. Therefore I spoke thus to them."

IT happened one day as they were studying that the Master said to his disciples: "I saw two bedizened she-demons entering a room to defile two youths who were in it. Now I had it in my power to save them. But inasmuch as they brought this on themselves by practicing witchcraft, I made no effort to save them. For thus said our sages, of blessed memory: 'He who seeks to defile himself, will find doors open to him.'" The disciples, on investigating the matter, found the Master's words to be true indeed.

IT happened one day that they were studying. In the middle of the discourse the Master called out: "Be silent!" Then he exclaimed: "Blessed be the true Judge!" The disciples asked why he spoke thus. He said to them: "Know that I heard a warning pro-claimed from heaven that the locust would attack throughout Safed, devouring every blade of grass, leaving no means of sustenance in Safed. And all this would come to pass because of one poor man, Rabbi Altaraz, who rages against the Holy One, Blessed Be He, because of the depth of his misfortune, and weeps in the bitterness of his soul. And His Blessed Name cannot withhold His wrath from his wicked neighbors who, though aware of his misery, yet have no pity upon him. Therefore was this evil decree pronounced upon them. In God's name, go collect from among you money and bring it to this poor man. Mayhap God will turn His thoughts to us that we shall not perish."

They thereupon collected from among them about five *gulden* and sent it to the poor man by one of their group, who found him in his house lying on the ground crying and weeping. The messenger asked him: "Why do you cry out?" And he answered: "Shall I not weep over my evil fortune, inasmuch as my livelihood and that of my family was that I was a drawer of water and would sell it. Today the rafters fell and my casks and jugs were broken. And I have no means with which to buy others in their stead. Therefore I cry out before the Lord. For am I more sinful than all the world?" Now, when the disciple found that the words of the Master were justified, he gave the poor man the money and said to him: "This evil decree befell us because of you. We beg you to forgive us and pray that the Lord annul this evil decree." The poor man then cast himself to the ground and prayed to the Lord to annul the decree. The disciple then returned and related

the matter to his colleagues. They resumed their studies and while they were so engaged, the earth grew dark and they lifted their eyes and beheld a great host of locusts and they were sore afraid. But the Master said to them: "Fear not, for this poor man has already forgiven you for his humiliation and the evil decree has been averted. Be not afraid." And the Lord turned an exceeding strong wind which took up the locusts and there remained not one locust in all of Safed. The Master then said: "Be you blessed of the Lord, for on your account was the decree averted." And from this day and thereafter all the people of Safed paid heed to the needs of this poor man.

IT happened one day that the Master said to his disciples: "Know ye that on the morrow we shall read a certain passage in the Book of Splendor which is very difficult to explain. Therefore, study it carefully." And they replied: "We shall do so." That night each one studied the passage diligently and in the morning when each asked the other for his interpretation, they found that each had arrived at the same sense of the text. They then remarked: "Can it be that the Master said that the passage was difficult without reason? Let us once again review the text." This they did several times and could not find any new meaning.

They sat down to study with the Master who asked them: "Do you all agree upon the meaning or has each of you arrived at a different explanation?" They answered: "We all interpret the passage alike and are surprised that our Master holds this passage to be difficult, whereas it appears to us to be merely a scribal error." He replied: "This is no error. Let one of you give me the explanation." One of the group began to present the meaning of the text they had all accepted. But even as he spoke, a flock of birds came and chirped incessantly. The Master then said to his disciple: "Be silent! These birds are the souls of righteous men who have come from the Garden of Eden to inform you that you are in error. For your understanding raises more questions than solutions. Be therefore silent and I will give you the correct explanation." When he had finished, the birds flew off and the disciples, embarrassed, said to each other: "Where is our understanding? How can we hide our shame? Were we blind not to see the problems?" To which the Master replied: "Even according to your interpretation, there have been revealed many hidden secrets; I spoke only in your merit and for the glory of those righteous men who had come."

IT happened one day as the Master was taking his mid-day rest and his lips moved in speech, that Rabbi Abraham Bruchim leaned over near the mouth of the Master to listen. The Ari awoke to find him standing over him. Said Rabbi Abraham: "Forgive me, Master. Seeing the lips of the *tsaddik* moving, I put my ear close to listen." The Ari laughed and said: "If only you knew what secret lore my soul received this night on the story of Balaam's ass! I call heaven and earth to witness that were I

16

to stay with you for eighty years, I could not tell you all of it." To which the disciples rejoined: "Why does not our Master write a book containing his wisdom?" He answered: "It is not possible, for all things are connected together. When I open my mouth to expound my thoughts, words rush forth as a gushing fountain, but I prefer that my words flow forth in a trickle so that you will be able to hear without any loss, lest you be like a babe who is choked from an overabundance of milk. How can I then write a book and impart to you my lore? Rather, let each one of you write what he has learned from me."

Now, in reality, permission to write had been given only to Rabbi Hayim Vital, who fully understood the teachings of the Master. Yet still each one used to write until it happened one day that Rabbi Moses Meshullam was called to the Torah to read the passage "and Moses wrote..." and when he descended from the reader's podium he came up to kiss the Master's hand. Said the Master to him: "Did I not admonish all of you not to write down my teachings?" Whereat they answered: "From the day that you charged us, O Master, we have not put down anything in writing." He replied: "Does the Torah, Heaven forbid, lie? For it states expressly 'and Moses wrote.' Moreover the booklets on your person testify that they are newly written by your own hand." The disciple was too frightened to answer.

IT happened one day as the Master was expounding the lesson that a disciple of Rabbi Moses Cordorevero pointed out a matter in which the Master's view differed from that of his teacher. Directing his glance to one side, the Master said: "Your teacher is sitting here and he tells me that you are misrepresenting his view." He replied, saying: "Can you prove it?" Directing his glance back to the disciple, he gave the view of Rabbi Moses, adding: "If you do not believe me, go to his house, look into this-and-this book on such-and-such a page. There you will find just what I have said." He did this and found that the words of the Master were true and returned and acknowledged that he was justified.

IT happened one day that Rabbi Samuel Useda entered the presence of the Master. The Master rose before him and, seating him at his right, conversed with him at some length. This provoked great amazement among the disciples. When Rabbi Samuel left, Rabbi Hayim Vital asked: "Why did you single him out for distinction today, seeing that you never did so on the many previous occasions when he visited you?" The Ari replied: "It was not before him that I arose, but before Rabbi Pinchas ben Jair who accompanied him because he had that day performed a good deed." And Rabbi Hayim Vital, on hearing this, arose and ran to overtake Rabbi Samuel and adjured him in this manner: "As our Master lives, please tell me what good deed did you perform this day that the Master should speak so well of you?" He replied: "This morning I arose early, as is my wont, to be one of the first ten in the synagogue.

I heard a sound of great weeping and turned aside to learn the cause of it. I saw that all who were present were naked and in tears. For that night thieves had entered and stolen all they possessed. My pity was aroused and I took off all my clothes and gave them to them. And the proof is that you see me now dressed in my Sabbath garments." On hearing this, Rabbi Hayim kissed him on the forehead and blessed him.

IT happened one day that the Master ordered one of his disciples to leave him. He left and all that day felt as one who had been severely chastised and wept and prayed to the Lord the entire day that his sins should not cause him to be banished from the Master's presence.

The next morning he came before the Master, crying and pleading to be told what wrong he had committed so that he might do penance. The Master said: "This is because of the chickens in your house. Three days now they have been without food and they cried out to the Lord. Therefore you have been under a ban from heaven. Now, therefore, if you will take it upon yourself and not depend on your wife, so that even before your morning prayers, you feed the chickens, I will unloose the ban." When the disciple accepted this judgment, he lifted the ban.

IT happened one day as they were at their studies that the Master asked his disciples: "Do you know so-and-so, the informer?" They replied: "May his name be blotted out." He then said: "Bring me a trap," which they did; and the Master set it in a certain place. Straightaway, a mouse was caught in it. The Master then spoke to the mouse in the presence of all: "Did you think that when you acted as an informer and a slanderer that there was, God forbid, neither Judge nor judgment in this world?"

The mouse then wept and implored him to pray to God that he might be spared from the great anguish of his soul's transmigrations and be immediately admitted to hell. But he said: "Get you gone from here. For you are not yet even worthy to enter hell." Whereat he opened the trap and let him out while the disciples looked on in amazement.

IT came to pass on a day that the Master and his disciples went to the memorial at the burial site of Shmaya and Abtalion. There he meditated on the oneness of God. When he had ended his meditation, he said, in the name of Shmaya and Abtalion, to his disciples, that they should pray that Messiah, the son of Joseph, should not die in their lifetime. In his great modesty he never revealed until the day he died that he himself was the Messiah.

IT happened one day that the Master required of one of his disciples to perform a *Yihud*—a deep meditation on the unity of God and the Shechinah—at the graves of all the

tsaddikim. Each *tsaddik* would then reveal to him hidden secrets on the one condition that he would neither address nor greet anyone. But though the disciple performed the required meditations, he received no revelation. Coming before the Master, he complained that the *tsaddikim* had revealed nothing. Whereat the Master rejoined: "Why did you not heed my word, inasmuch as in one place you did greet a person?" The disciple at once admitted the truth of the Master's words.

ONE day the Master entrusted to Rabbi Hayim Vital a *Yihud* to be performed at the graves of Abaye and Rabba in Avnit. Having done so, Rabbi Hayim returned to the Master, who raised himself to his full height before him and showed him great honor. Taken aback, Rabbi Hayim Vital cried out: "Why the unusual distinction this day?" "I rose, not in your honor, but out of respect for Benayahu ben Yehoyada, who entered with you." Said Rabbi Hayim: "Master, not so! The meditation was for Abaya and Rabba, who should have come, and not Benayahu." The Master then said to him: "Know that at the place where you sat down to repeat the *Yihud*, there Benayahu ben Yehoyada is buried. And seeing that the meditation affected the very source of his soul, he did therefore accompany you."

Soon thereafter, the Master went with his disciples to Avnit. And at one point in the journey the Master said to Rabbi Hayim Vital: "Here lies buried Benayahu, of blessed memory, and here you sat down to repeat the med-

itation." Thereupon did Rabbi Hayim recollect and acknowledge the truth of the Master's words.

IT happened one Purim eve that Rabbi Hayim Vital called unto him a widow who was his neighbor. He said to her: "Take two gold pieces for your trouble and tomorrow appear before the Master with your daughter and ask him for Purim money. Now, when the Master will say: 'Give it to her,' you shall tell him: 'The charity I seek is that you look into my daughter's palm and read her fortune.'" Now Rabbi Hayim was being subtle, inasmuch as he had often urged the Master to instruct him in the art of palmistry, but the Master would always put him off. But now, when the Master would announce that such-and-such a line signifies wealth or the like, Rabbi Hayim himself would learn. In the morning, as the Master was expounding to his disciples the laws of Purim, the woman appeared and said: "My Master knows that it is customary to give to him who puts forth his hand for alms. How much more so is this the case for a widow like me!" The Master said: "Let her have her request so that we will thereby fulfill the requirement of Purim gift-giving." Whereat the woman replied: "Although I am a widow, I am not that poor, since I support myself by the labor of my hands. But do only this kindness for me. Look into the palm of my only daughter and tell her fortune." The Master called out: "The trickery of Rabbi Hayim will not avail him in this matter. For I know that he

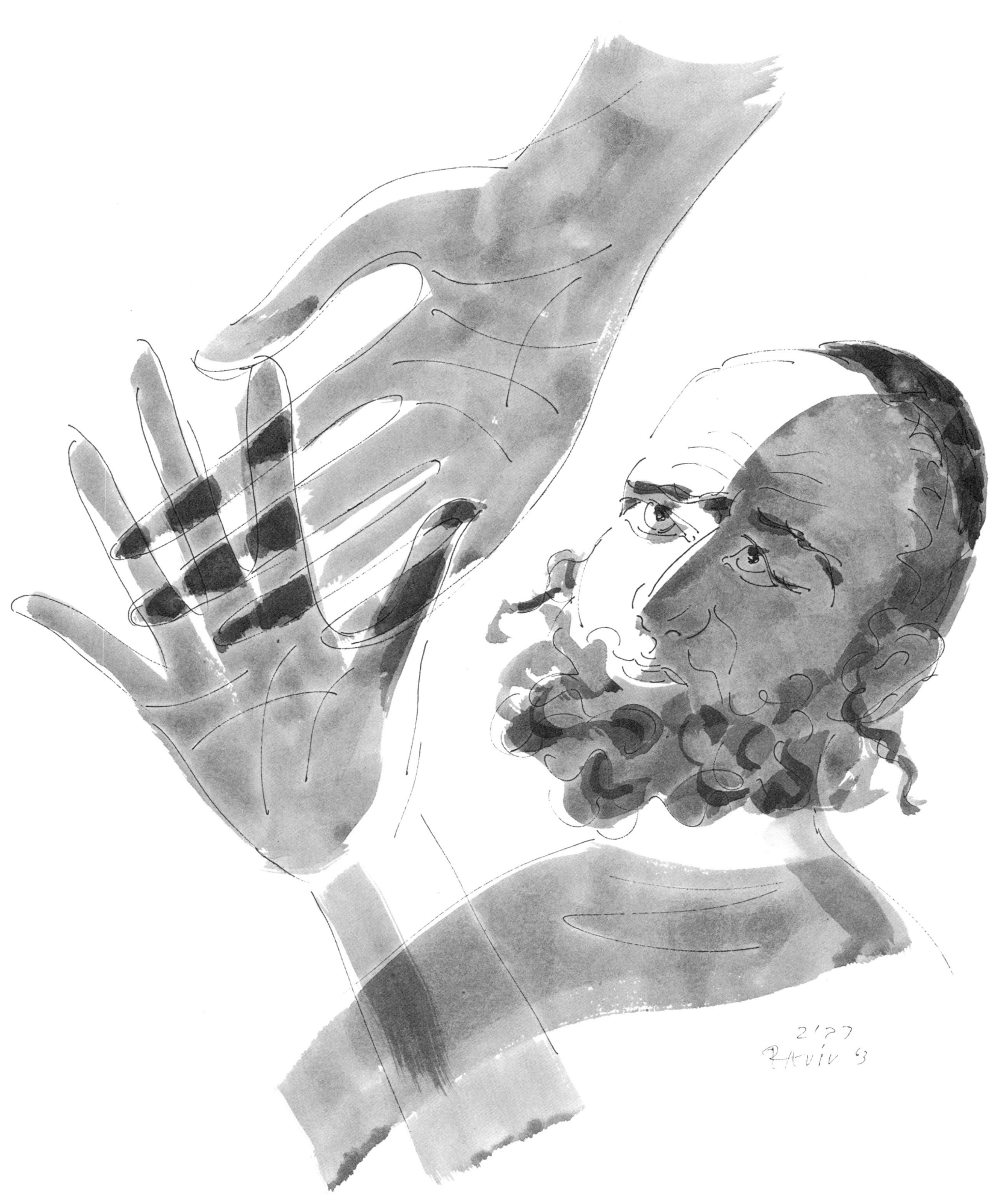

prompted you to speak thus. Nevertheless I will not let you depart empty-handed. Let your daughter move back some distance and place her hand on the reader's podium and I will tell her fortune." When she had done this, he revealed to her all that had happened to her from the day of her birth and what awaited her till the day of her death. Rabbi Hayim was overwhelmed with awe and never again sought to acquire this art. And the Master said to him: "Have I not told you that it is enough for you to study the Kabbalah, for through it you will know all things."

IT happened in Safed that some young men were out for a stroll. As they sat down, they saw a finger emerge from the earth and disappear into it. One of them said by way of jest: "Who will put a marriage ring on this finger?" One youth rose up and set his ring upon the finger, which thereupon sank back into the ground together with the ring. Struck with awe, the young men returned to the city. In the course of time the matter was forgotten. Somewhat later, the youth betrothed a maiden. On the day of the wedding, a multitude gathered to celebrate the nuptials. Suddenly a woman cried out: "What blemish does the bridegroom find in me that he should desire to take unto himself another, seeing that he had already consecrated me unto him? If justice be done to me, well and good; but if not, I will kill the groom and the bride. See this ring in my hand," she added, showing it to the guests, who recognized the name of the groom engraved in it.

Thereupon the father of the bride took his daughter to his house and the wedding joy was turned to mourning, while the strange woman remained with the bridegroom.

The Master then sent for the youth and spoke with him privately, asking him: "Do you or do you not desire to be married to this demon? Have no fear, for I will save you from her." The youth answered: "Who would be so foolish as to want to marry a demon! Alas for my bad luck! If only I had broken a leg that day so that I could not have gone on that stroll!" The Master said: "Sit here," and instructed his beadle to invite the demon to judgment before him. When the beadle searched throughout the house and did not find her, he returned to the Master and said: "She is not to be found." But the Master said: "She is surely in the house but because of her fear she has hidden from you. Go back and when you get to the ladder leading to the attic, call out: 'I am a messenger from the Master. If you return with me—well and good. But if you do not, he will place you and your family under a ban.'"

The beadle did as he was told. When he had said what he was told to say, the woman came down and followed him to the Master, who said to her: "What do you want from this youth? Why do you not get married to a demon of your own kind?" To which the woman replied: "Is this in accordance with the law, that after he consecrated me, I can be married to another?" He answered: "This marriage was an error. He did not see your face and could not know that you are a demon. It was just in fun that he put his ring on your finger." Nonetheless she kept up a constant argument till

the Master rebuked her, saying: "No matter what the law, I will see that he gives you a divorce, and should you refuse to accept it, I will place you and all that is yours under a ban." He at once called in the scribe and drew up the bill of divorce, which she accepted. The Master then besware her with a most stringent oath that she not harm either the bridegroom or the bride. When she left, the Master sent for the father of the bride and arranged for the return of the betrothed to the youth.

IT happened one day that they were studying a portion of the Book of Splendor. The Master observed: "Here lies hidden a deep secret, and it is too dangerous to permit myself to reveal it." His disciples, joined by Rabbi Hayim Vital, paid no heed but pressed him till he interpreted the passage. And when he had finished, he said: "How many times have I told you that this is perilous but you would not heed my voice. Now it has been decreed that my son Moses shall die within seven days." On hearing this, the disciples were sorely disturbed. The Master arose, returned to his house and asked his wife concerning his son Moses. She replied: "About an hour ago he returned from school with a headache and even now is lying in bed." The Master went up to his room and saw that he was consumed with fever and at once realized that he would die. Even before the week was up, the boy died. The disciples were deeply grieved. After his period of mourning, the Master sent for them, for they were too ashamed to come before him. He told them:

"Have no fear that because of my son's death I will hold back anything from you. Even if I knew that all my children would, God forbid, die, I would not withhold aught from you." Thereupon they fell to his feet and cried out: "Long live the Master."

IT happened one day that Rabbi Moses Alsheikh came before the Master, complaining: "Wherein have I sinned, that the Master puts me off with mere words, and why can I not be as one of his disciples?" The Master replied: "Have I not already told you that you have come into this world to perfect the simple interpretation—*pshat*—of the Torah. The esoteric meaning—*sod*—was already given in another age at the time of Huzpit Haturgaman, of whose soul you are a spark. And should you doubt me, tomorrow is Sabbath Eve. Go, sit in a certain spot where we will pass on our way to greet the Sabbath. If you see us as we go by, you will know that you have not attained this knowledge." Rabbi Alsheikh accepted the proposal.

The next morning he purchased the necessities for the Sabbath and before noon put on his Sabbath garments and went and sat in the spot of which the Master had spoken. All day long he waited and at the moment the Master passed by, he fell asleep. The Master came and returned but he saw him not. The Master then told his disciples to awaken him, lest he be killed by the villagers. They woke him and he arose bewildered. He exclaimed: "How is it that all day I sat waiting, and just now sleep

overcame me!" Said the Master: "Did I not tell you that this would happen? Rather be heartened by your written work, which will illumine the eyes of the world."

It was through such occurrences that the fame of the Ari was spread throughout the world.

NOW there were some men from Constantinople who had come to pay their respects to the saintly men of Safed. There they beheld the greatness of the Master, and on returning to Constantinople they recounted some of his praises. In Constantinople there lived a rich man who had indulged in all manner of transgressions. When he heard of the Master, he said: "Let me go to Safed and see whether the Master can tell me what evil I have done, so that I may find repentence through him." He departed his city and put up at an inn. He drank a cup of wine in a toast to the Master. This was designed to put the Master to a test. Now the Master, who then was engaged in a discourse, broke out in laughter. "Why do you laugh?" asked his disciples. He answered: "Know that a rich man has come out of Constantinople and is now lodged in a certain inn and he holds a cup of wine. To put me to the test, he has drunk the wine in a toast to you and me. Such-and-such is his appearance and on such-and-such a day will he come here. Now let you all show him regard, seeing that in him abides the great soul of Ahab King of Israel." The rich man came before the Master in Safed and was shown great honor. He said to the Master: "If you can tell me all that I have done, I will become a penitent; but if not, then I will say that there is, God forbid, no Judge and no justice." The Master told his disciples to leave them, for he did not wish to embarrass the rich man. He then recounted to his visitor in minute detail each depravity in which he had indulged, not sparing a single detail, and the rich man was affrighted and exclaimed: "Verily I have sinned, and because of you I shall do penance." He then gave the Master an offering, sent for his wife and children, and died in Safed, fully penitent.

YET still another tale is told of a rich man who came before the Master and said: "Are you the seer who knows the most secret deeds of a man?" He answered: "I am." The visitor said: "If you can tell me all my past misdeeds, I will accept penance; but if not, I shall no longer believe in God." The Master, peering closely at him, told him all that he had done from the day he was born and also said that he had sinned with his maidservant. The man admitted everything save the sin with the maidservant, which he denied. Said the Master: "And if I show her to you what will you then say?" And at once setting his hand on him, he drew her forth. When the man saw her and recognized her, he almost fainted. He fell at the feet of the Master and cried out: "I have sinned and indeed greatly transgressed." The Master revived him but he continued to call out bitterly, pleading that her spirit be removed from him. The Master then said to him: "Our

2/27
RAVIV 65

sages have taught that he who joins himself unto a loose woman is bound up with her as though to a dog. Both in this world and in the next she clings to him and does not leave him save he do great penance and acts of expiation." The man avowed that he was prepared even for the four judgments of death of the High Court. The Master declared: "Your penance is by fire." Immediately the man took out coins to buy wood for the burning. But the Master demurred: "Our executions differ from those of other nations. The law requires hot lead." Said the man: "Let come what may. I am ready to die." The Master ordered lead to be bought and put over a fire. He then instructed the man to say his confession of sin, and he complied. The Master said: "Throw yourself to the ground," and he threw himself to the ground. "Stretch forth your feet!" and he stretched them. "Stretch forth your hands!" and he stretched them. "Shut your eyes!" and he shut them. "Open your mouth!" and he opened it. The Master poured into his mouth all manner of sweets which he had prepared and said to him: " 'Thine iniquity is taken away and thy sin expiated' (Isaiah 6). You shall not die." He then raised him up from the ground and prescribed his penances. Among these it was required of him to read each day five pages from the Book of Splendor, albeit he might not even understand. The man then sent for his wife and children and died in Safed, fully penitent.

I T happened one day that a youth came to the Master, kissed his feet and said: "I need to go abroad. Please tell me what will happen to me." The Master answered: "May the Lord be with you. Go in peace and there you will take unto you a beautiful wife with a rich dowry. But when you have been married to her for six months, she will die and you will inherit from her only 600 gold pieces. And this is the reason. In a former state of existence, this woman was, like you, a man, who was your friend and yet caused you distress for six months. Finally he brought suit against you in the civil courts and caused you to lose 600 gold pieces. And now he has come to make atonement to you. As against the six months of your distress, you may take pleasure in her beauty, and as for the inheritance, it is to repay you for the 600 gold pieces he caused you to lose. Nevertheless you should show forbearance and forgive." All this came to pass as the Master had foretold.

I T happened one day that the Master said to his disciples: "Tomorrow you may go a-picnicking with food and drink on condition that you invite along the rabbi who is the author of *Weeping Voices*." They agreed. He then added: "Go invite him at once, before he takes it upon himself to fast. For should he do so, he is not likely to release himself from his vow." Rabbi Hayim Vital and two of the disciples went to this rabbi, who greeted them: "God's blessing upon you. Why did you leave your Master and come to me?" They answered: "We have come to invite you to accompany us tomorrow on a walk." He asked them: "Why did you come today and not tomorrow?" And

they replied: "So that you would not meantime impose on yourself a fast, since you never seek release from a vow." At this he scoffed: "If such is the perceptiveness of your Master, it is as naught." Said Rabbi Hayim Vital: "Enough of this small talk. Let our Master be what he may, but will you come with us tomorrow?" He agreed to join them.

The next morning they sent after him and he went with them to Ayn Hazaytim to the grave of Rabbi Judah bar Ilai. As they sat in discourse on the Torah, the Master came and they all rose up before him. The rabbi showed him exceptional deference and seated him on his left. After a while, the Master arose and delivered a discourse. When he had ended, he recited the Kaddish and sat down. "Were my words pleasing to you?" he asked. "Not especially," came the reply. "And why not?" To which the rabbi replied: "Because I see many difficulties in your lesson. For example, in such and such a matter you held a view the reverse of that of Rabbi Simeon bar Johai." And so he challenged the Master on many other points. Thereat the Master turned to his disciples, for he saw great bewilderment in their faces that one could so challenge the Master, and said: "Such a scholar is to be praised, not like you who agree with everything." Turning to the rabbi, he said: "Please restate your problem," and went on to answer all his questions. The rabbi posed problems and at the same time cited authorities to uphold his views. But the Master bade him be brief. "State your questions quickly that I may answer them, for my disciples are famished and want to eat." He answered: "Just a minute," and sat down for a while. The Master pressed him to finish asking so that he might answer. The rabbi then arose and cried out: "You have prevailed. I have no more questions to ask you. My congratulations, Master. And now, will you please sit at the head of the table, for until this moment I held you as lower than the least of my students, but now I know that the spirit of the Lord is in you." Reluctantly the Master took his place at the head of the table and they ate and drank joyfully and returned to the city.

When they were about to leave each other, the Master spoke first: "Sleep well." And the rabbi replied: "May we both rest well. But I shall not leave you until you prescribe a penance for my soul." But the Master put him off with words and departed. On the morrow the rabbi returned to the Master, who rose to his full height before him and seated him with great honor. "I have come," said the rabbi, "so that you may give me a penance." The Master replied: "God forbid! Who am I that I should prescribe a penance for your eminence!" Said the rabbi: "Have I not always spoken as my heart dictates? At first I did not believe your great repute, but now I have seen with my own eyes." He urged so strongly that the Master finally said: "Your penance is very heavy and you may not be able to perform it." He replied: "I swear that even if my penance were one of the four deaths set by the Court, I should accept and be ready to die." The Master then said: "I call heaven and earth to witness that I have seen no other who is as free of sin as you. What penance can I give you? Your penance shall be to eat each day a fine fat fowl and to meditate on the Torah; and may the fasts which

your eminence had taken upon himself be as those to which the sages, of blessed memory, had reference." (When a young scholar takes upon himself a private fast in order to afflict himself, it is as though he had committed a sin.) He then kissed the Master and went out from before him rejoicing and glad of heart. He went home and prepared a great feast to which he invited the Master and his disciples.

He also invited the most eminent sage of that generation, the *gaon* Rabbi Moses Galanti, of blessed memory, who remarked: "What is so exceptional about this day?" To which he replied: "I have invited Rabbi Isaac Ashkenazi to a feast which I have prepared for him." "Have you tested him and found in him the word of the Lord?" He then recounted all that had happened. Rabbi Moses said: "In this case it is indeed a *mitzvah* to attend this feast." When he came through the door, the Master and his disciples rose to their feet before him and showed him great honor, urging him to sit at the head. After much entreaty, the *gaon* sat at the head of the table and they rejoiced each in the other and they did eat and drink. When the feast was ended, each went to his own house.

In the morning the *gaon* arose and went to the Master's house. And Rabbi Isaac trembled with fear on seeing him and said: "Does your excellency begrudge me my life that you want to bring about my death? Why did you put yourself to the trouble of coming to me? You should have sent for me and I would have come to you." He replied: "Your modesty is most exemplary. I have come to you that you should set a penance for my soul." The Master said: "What am I and what is my life that I should

set a penance for your excellency! I adjure you if you value my life to let me be!" Said Rabbi Moses: "Do I not have it in my power to beswear you, by the sacred Name, that you tell me all that you see on my forehead? I entreat you to tell me before I grow angry." The Master looked into his face and said: "Your honesty is suspect."

On hearing this, the *gaon* went home, took off his clothes, and put on sackcloth and ashes. He then sat on the ground and lifted his voice in a great outcry: "Where shall I hide my shame, seeing that I am a judge in Safed, and yet my honesty is in question." He cried until he had no more strength to cry. And all his household looked on astonished. He asked for some water to restore his soul and ordered his beadle to call together all his workers, men and women, who were employed by him to make clothes. When they assembled before him, they were amazed to find him seated in sackcloth. He said: "Please heed my word. Give me an account of what I owe you." They all replied with one voice: "Not one of us knows how to keep an account. Indeed, whatever money we receive from you, carries a special blessing so that we have enough for food, drink and clothing and even more. Therefore what accounting do we need with you? Indeed, from the day we began to work for you, we have kept no record of the money you have given us. How can we then know how much it came to!" Then the *gaon* cried out: "Verily this matter is now clear. But surely you understand that there are in this world both Judge and justice. Therefore do I sit in this fashion. This is my punishment, for I am but a mortal being. Now therefore, if

henceforth you agree to be very exact in your accounting, even to the smallest sum—well and good. But if not, I will dispose of my business. For I do not want, by my own dealings, to be doomed to suffer in hell. And now to take care of past misdealings, here is a heap of coins; take as much as you want." They answered: "Master, what can we take, inasmuch as we do not know of any account? Is dishonesty permissible unto us?" He replied: "I will make an agreement with you that you take what you want and declare with a good conscience: 'We have received all that is due us from the day we started to work and if perchance more is due us, we forgive you freely.' And I, too, will say likewise."

Immediately they all forgave him and not one of them took as much as a penny, save one woman who took two piasters. He urged her to take more but she refused. Then they all departed. The sage got dressed and went to the house of the Master, who met him on the way. The Master exclaimed: "Why all the excitement?" "Is even a suspicion of dishonesty a small matter in your eyes?" cried the sage. Said the Master: "It is all past." Said the sage: "See if any more atoning is needed." He replied: "Nothing more." The sage asked: "But wherein was I suspect?" He replied: "It concerned the woman who took the two piasters. And herein lay the error: This woman, being a weaver of fine cloth, should have received more in wages than the other weavers, but you paid her like the weavers of coarse cloth." Whereupon he kissed the Master and blessed him and made for him a great feast. And thereafter he held him in great esteem.

THE story is told that one day there appeared before the Master, the sage Rabbi Jacob Abulafia. The Master greeted him, saying: "Your excellency wishes to go to Egypt and desires that I write him a letter of introduction." "Yes," he replied. The Master said: "Go in peace. There is a pressing need that you go." Rabbi Jacob asked: "What is the great need, since I am not going for any charitable purpose?" He replied: "When you return, you will know." Whereupon he wrote for him the letter and gave it to him, saying: "Let it speed your going." And so he went to Egypt where, in honor of the Master, they showed him great esteem. When he was ready to return by camel, one of his friends said: "Why should you ride on a camel—which is a difficult thing? Rather buy an animal more fit for human travel and go comfortably with the horsemen." And so he did. He went out with the caravan and imitated the ways of the horsemen. One day when the horsemen rested as was their custom, the sage did likewise. He fell into a deep sleep. When the camel caravan overtook them, they arose and waked Rabbi Jacob. He arose, unloosed his donkey, who followed the caravan, while he himself slept on for two more hours. When he awoke, he found himself alone. He became frightened and in his great anxiety ran along the road. Toward evening he saw men plowing. He felt relieved and said: "I will join them." He ran toward them and coming up with them sat down for a little while. He saw a plowman beating the oxen mercilessly. Soon he

beheld the plowman turn into an ox and the ox became a man, who then placed the ox in a yoke and began to beat him. This transformation repeated itself several times. The sage was frightened but could not flee for he did not know the way and was in great distress. When the sun set, the three became human beings. They lifted their voices in weeping and greeted him, saying: "Is your excellency from Safed?" He replied: "I am." "Does Rabbi Ashkenazi live in Safed?" "He does." They fell at his feet and wept, and the sage wept with them. They asked: "Did your excellency see our plight?" He answered: "I did." They pleaded with him: "For the sake of God, have pity on us. We are Jews. When you come to Safed, go at once to the Master and ask him to set a penance for us, for we can no longer endure our troubles." And the sage replied: "I shall do as you ask." They then swore with a binding oath that they would perform whatever penance the Master imposed upon them, and before an eye could blink, they had set him once again in the midst of the caravan. And his spirit revived in him.

When he arrived in Safed, he went at once to the Master, who welcomed him with these words: "I know that you have come to me concerning the oxen. Please come back tomorrow." On the next day the Master spoke to him: "Now your excellency will understand why it was so necessary for you to go down to Egypt. For your soul is bound up in their souls." The sage asked: "What was their sin?" He answered: "They marred the corners of their heads." "But what connection is there between the corners of the head and oxen?" The Master replied: "You have not read the sacred writings." Said the sage: "But, Master, this is neither to be found in the Gemara nor the Midrash." The Master replied: "It is expressly stated in Scripture." "But this verse is not found in the Torah!" Whereat the Master rejoined: "It relates to the initial letters of the Hebrew text—'pe' and 'resh' which together spell 'par' meaning an ox. This indicates that he who rounds the corners of his head will be turned into an ox. You must therefore fast tomorrow and direct your meditation to the souls of these creatures." And in this fashion the Master prescribed for him all the penances—self-afflictions that had to be performed so that these beings would be brought to a state of perfection. They appeared to the sage in a dream and said to him: "May your mind be at rest even as our souls have found rest from that day on which you began to perform the penances prescribed for you by the Master. For by your first penance we were brought forth out of the hard labor in which you saw us engaged and led into *Gehinnom*. And by each additional penance which you performed for us we were freed from a heavy yoke to a lighter one until at long last we were admitted into the Garden of Eden."

IT is told that once on a Sabbath eve just before the Sabbath queen arrived, the Master and his disciples went forth from the city of Safed dressed in white garments to welcome the Sabbath. The Master began to sing a Psalm of David—"Ascribe unto the Lord ye sons of the mighty"—and a hymn

כליבי

RAVIV '64

specially composed for the welcome of the Sabbath; and also the Psalms: "A song for the Sabbath Day" and "The Lord reigneth—in a sweet melody." While they were singing, the Master asked his disciples: "Friends, would you like to go with me to Jerusalem before the Sabbath, so that we may celebrate the Sabbath in Jerusalem?" (Now Jerusalem was more than twenty-five parasangs from Safed.) Some of the disciples spoke in reply: "We readily agree." Whereas some answered: "Let us first tell our wives and then we shall go." Thereat the Master was seized with a violent trembling and smote his hands together and cried out: "Woe unto us. We have not merited to be redeemed. Inasmuch as you tarried, the exile, because of the greatness of our sins, is once again firmly entrenched. Had you all in one voice cried out that you gladly agree to go, then straightaway would all Israel have been redeemed, for the hour was ripe for our redemption."

A story of great moment is told about a wandering soul in the days of our Master and Teacher, the holy, saintly man of God, Rabbi Isaac Luria Ashkenazi, of eternally blessed memory; to give proof that there is justice and there is a Judge and that there is no forgetfulness before the throne of His glory, and that everything is founded upon uprightness and justice. Yet is He slow to anger, showing forbearance to the wicked.

Now this is what came to pass at the time of the holy, pure, godly kabbalist, Rabbi Isaac Luria Ashkenazi, in Safed. It happened that a spirit entered into a widow and tormented her mightily. Now men would come in and speak to the spirit, who would give answer to each according to his question. Among those who came was a sage who was a disciple of the Ari and his name was Yosef Arzin. The spirit greeted him with these words: "Baruch haba! Welcome, my teacher and master. Surely you must remember that I was once your disciple in Egypt." On hearing his name and the name of his father, the sage recognized him and departed.

When the relatives of the widow saw how great was her anguish, they went to the Master, Rabbi Isaac Luria, and entreated him to drive out the spirit from the woman. However, since the Master had no time to go himself, he sent his disciple, Rabbi Hayim Vital, of blessed memory, giving him power by means of certain names and talismanic charms and enjoining upon him to drive out the spirit against its wishes through oaths and the ban. As soon as Rabbi Hayim Vital entered, the woman turned her face away from him to the wall. Rabbi Hayim Vital cried out: "Evil one, why do you turn away from me?" The spirit replied: "I cannot gaze upon you, for the wicked are not able to look upon the Divine Countenance." Rabbi Hayim Vital commanded the spirit to turn about at once, and it obeyed. The rabbi then asked: "What sin did you commit that you are so heavily punished?" It answered: "I sinned with the wife of another man and begot bastard children and for twenty-five years I have been wandering about in torment on the face of the

earth. And I can find no rest. For three destroying angels accompany me everywhere and punish me and beat me and proclaim publicly: 'Thus shall be done to the man who begot many bastards in Israel.' And these three evil angels are alluded to in the verse: 'Set Thou a wicked man over him; and let an adversary stand at his right hand.' Do you not see one of these angels standing at my right and a second at my left making their proclamation while the third beats me mercilessly?"

"But surely," exclaimed Rabbi Hayim Vital, "have not our sages, of blessed memory, said: 'The punishment of the wicked in *Gehinnom* endures for twelve months!'" The spirit replied: "You do not appear to understand the meaning of that passage. Its real significance is that the wicked first suffer all kinds of agony outside of *Gehinnom;* then they are brought into *Gehinnom*, where they remain for twelve months and are cleansed and purified of all their sins until their souls are entirely free of blemish, so that they may be fully prepared to enter *Gan Eden*. It is as if an experienced physician first puts on the wounds strong and stinging medicaments which consume the raw flesh. He then applies to the wounds healing ointments that cool the flesh and restore it as it was at first. So it is with regard to *Gehinnom*. For the torment of *Gehinnom* is not even a sixtieth part of what the sinful soul suffers before entering *Gehinnom*."

Rabbi Hayim Vital then inquired: "What was the manner of your death?" To which it replied: "By strangulation. For, as is indicated in *Ketubot* 30a, 'even though the Sanhedrin was abolished, the four death sentences were not abolished.' In Alexandria I boarded a ship to go to Rashit. At the point where the Nile enters the sea, my ship capsized and sank and I drowned."

Thereupon Rabbi Hayim, of blessed memory, asked: "Why did you not recite the confessional? For had you confessed all your sins at the moment your soul departed your body, it might have helped you." The spirit answered sadly: "Woe is me. I had no time to confess. For the waters immediately came into my throat and strangled me. Moreover, as soon as the waters encompassed me, I lost consciousness." Rabbi Hayim asked: "What happened to you after you expired?" "When the news of the shipwreck reached Rashit, the Jews of that city came out to the water's edge and recovered the bodies of all the Jews who had drowned and buried us in the cemetery. And no sooner had the Jews left the cemetery, when a merciless angel came and beat mightily upon my grave with a rod of fire, so that my grave burst open. Whereupon the angel cried out: 'Evildoer, arise for justice.' He then placed me in a sling and cast me from Rashit to the gates of *Gehinnom*. As soon as I fell within the gates of *Gehinnom*, myriads of souls of evildoers who were doomed to hell went forth and all of them reviled me, shouting: 'Begone, begone, thou man of blood. Begone, thou troubler of Israel. You are not yet worthy nor are you yet permitted to enter *Gehinnom*.' I roamed from mountain to mountain and from hill to hill while these three destroying angels accompanied me always, proclaiming my punishment before me, all the while incessantly beating me. And constantly new

2/20
RAVIV 63

bands of destroying angels came upon me together with evil spirits all of whom heard the proclamation and added their blows upon me. One would pull me to him and then his fellow would in turn pull me to him and the links of my soul were torn asunder.

"And so I wandered till I came to Hurmiz, a big city, beyond Babylonia, near India. I intended to enter the body of some Jew in order to be spared these blows and afflictions. But when I discovered that these Jews were evildoers and sinners unto the Lord, living in sin with gentile women and committing other manifold transgressions, I could not by any means allow myself to enter into any one of them. Had I entered any one of these, I would have added his defilement and his wrongdoing to mine. And so I practiced caution and roamed from mountain to hill and from hill to mountain for many years until I arrived at the Wilderness of Judah. There I found a pregnant hind and because of the many afflictions that beset me, I entered into her. For by now seven years of misery had passed over me.

"But even after I came into the hind, I suffered greatly. For the soul of a human and the soul of a beast are not compatible. For the one walks upright and the other on all fours. Moreover, the soul of the beast is filled with impurity and is disgusting and evil-smelling in the eyes of man. Besides, its food differs from that of man. Added to these was the distress I felt because of the embryo she bore within her. The hind, too, suffered greatly, for three spirits cannot dwell at ease in one body. Because of this, her belly swelled until she burst and died. Then I went out of her and came to the city of Shechem, in the Land of Israel, and entered the body of a Jewish *Kohen*, who sent at once for Moslem holy men. I could not tolerate the many spells of these sources of defilement and the amulets which they hung on my neck, and I swiftly went from there."

Rabbi Hayim Vital then asked: "Do sources of defilement have the power to harm or heal of themselves?" It replied: "No. But because of the mass of impurity that the enchanters had implanted in the body of this Jewish *Kohen*, I realized that if I remained there, all these would cleave unto me. I could, therefore, not abide there and immediately fled to Safed —may it be built up and firmly established speedily in our day—and I entered the body of this woman. And I have suffered this affliction a full twenty-five years."

Rabbi Hayim then asked: "How long must you endure this anguish? Is there no release from it?" The spirit replied: "Not till all the bastard children whom I begat die. For as long as they live, I have no relief." At this the great multitude who were present cried exceedingly for they were overcome by fear and trembling and the dread of dire punishment. And this event caused a great spiritual awakening throughout the land. Then Rabbi Hayim asked: "Who was it that gave you permission to enter into this woman?" The spirit answered: "One night I lodged in her house. At dawn she arose from her bed and wanted to kindle a fire with stone and flint. But try as she would, the rags she used for kindling would not catch fire. She became exasperated and, throwing the flint and the stone to the ground,

called out in anger: 'Go to the devil!' And this word 'devil' gave me the opportunity to enter into her, seeing that I had already received permission to do this from the demon angels."

Whereupon Rabbi Hayim called out in great astonishment: "And is it for a sin such as this that you were allowed to enter her person?" Said the spirit: "For this and also because her appearance belies her sincerity, for she does not believe in the miracle of the exodus from Egypt at all. And on Passover, even when all Israel rejoices and recites the *Hallel* and tells the story of the exodus, all this is deemed by her to be vanity, mockery, and derision. And she thinks in her heart that this miracle never happened."

Forthwith the rabbi queried the woman: "Do you believe in full faith that the Holy One, Blessed Be He, created heaven and earth and that He has it within His power to do all He desires and that none may say: 'What doest Thou?' " She answered: "I believe." Again the rabbi asked: "Do you believe that the Holy One, Blessed Be He, brought us forth out of Egypt and split the sea for us?" She said: "I do." The rabbi further asked: "Do you believe all this with a perfect faith and do you repent and do you regret your former deeds?" "I do," she said, and began to cry. Thereat Rabbi Hayim laid a ban upon this spirit, decreeing that it leave the body through no other limb save the small toe of the left foot. (For it is well known that the limb from which the evil spirit makes its exit withers and shrivels entirely.) Then the rabbi pronounced the secret holy names which his Master had imparted to him. And at once the small toe swelled to the size of

a beet, and the spirit departed by way of it and vanished. But many nights thereafter the spirit came to the windows and the door of her house and frightened the woman. Her relatives then went to the Master, who once again sent his disciple, Rabbi Hayim Vital, of blessed memory, to investigate the state of the *mezuza* on the door. When he came there he found the door lintel altogether lacking a *mezuza*. Thereupon the Master commanded that a *mezuza* be affixed to the lintel. This was done and henceforth and forever after the evil spirit did not return.

IT is told that in the days of our Master, the Ari, of blessed memory, there lived in Safed a lad of eighteen who was the nephew of the sage Rabbi Joshua bin Nun. One day while he was studying at the yeshiva, the Master—may he be remembered for life everlasting—saw him and said to his father: "Know that your son is possessed by a certain spirit; therefore I advise you not to spend money needlessly on physicians." His father replied: "God forbid! He only suffers at times from a pain in his heart. This pain has been with him now for ten years. Time and again the doctors treat him and the pain goes away; and when it returns, the doctors renew the treatment." Said the Master to the lad's father: "I assure you that this is a spirit." And straightaway he gave orders to the spirit. The spirit began to speak and told him that he had dwelt within the lad for ten years. The Master asked: "Why did you tarry within him these many years?" The

spirit explained: "I was a pauper who dwelt in Rome and in that incarnation was supported through alms. At that time this lad was the steward of alms and when I pleaded with him to provide my sustenance, he refused. And I died of hunger. Now the heavenly court has decreed that even as he caused my death in that incarnation, so should I bring about his death in this one." Whereat the Master enjoined him from harming the lad in any manner and ordered him to depart. To this the spirit replied: "If your excellency wishes that I leave the lad, I make one condition, namely, that after I leave, this lad shall not look upon a women's face for three full days. And should he fail to carry out this condition, I shall kill him." The spirit then departed.

The lad's father inquired: "How do you feel, my son?" He replied: "I feel fine." "Really?" asked the father. The lad said: "Indeed, father, I feel even better than I felt before, when I took all those medicines." The Master then instructed that the lad be carefully guarded, and that he not be allowed to leave the house of study nor have women come near him. For he said that this spirit was full of guile and had set a condition which was very difficult to keep.

Now one of those three days happened to be *Rosh Hodesh* and Rabbi Hayim Vital went to prepare a feast and left Rabbi Joshua bin Nun in his stead to guard the lad. Later he too went out and left the lad alone. The lad's mother and his aunt came to visit him and, on seeing him, kissed him. At that very moment the spirit returned, entered into him, and choked him.

And lest the nations of the world put out a report that the Jews had slain him, the Master, of blessed memory, wrought miraculously and went to Tiberias on two stalks in the twinkling of an eye. This happened at twilight. And there in Tiberias our Master—may he be remembered for life everlasting—prayed that a report of this matter should not reach the nations of the world and no harm overtake any Jew. And after a sojourn of eight days, our Master returned to Safed.

THE tale is told that, at the time of my Master, of everlasting memory, we were sitting one day in his house of study, and a woman was brought before him to ascertain whether she was sick or had been possessed by a spirit. My Master was informed that she had never been sick or suffered pain, but suddenly she had changed and her whole body had been seized by tremors. My Master felt her pulse and stated that a spirit had possessed her. He sent her home. He then told me to go in the evening to exorcise the spirit. Moreover, he warned me to be on my guard, for this spirit was very sly and would lie to me at least three times when I asked its name. He also gave me certain charms by which to drive out the spirit.

Just before I entered this woman's house the spirit told the bystanders: "You will see that now Rabbi Hayim Vital will come to drive me from here. We shall see what his strength is and what he can do. I am not afraid of him, for what power has he to drive me out of here?" When I entered and greeted everyone, the

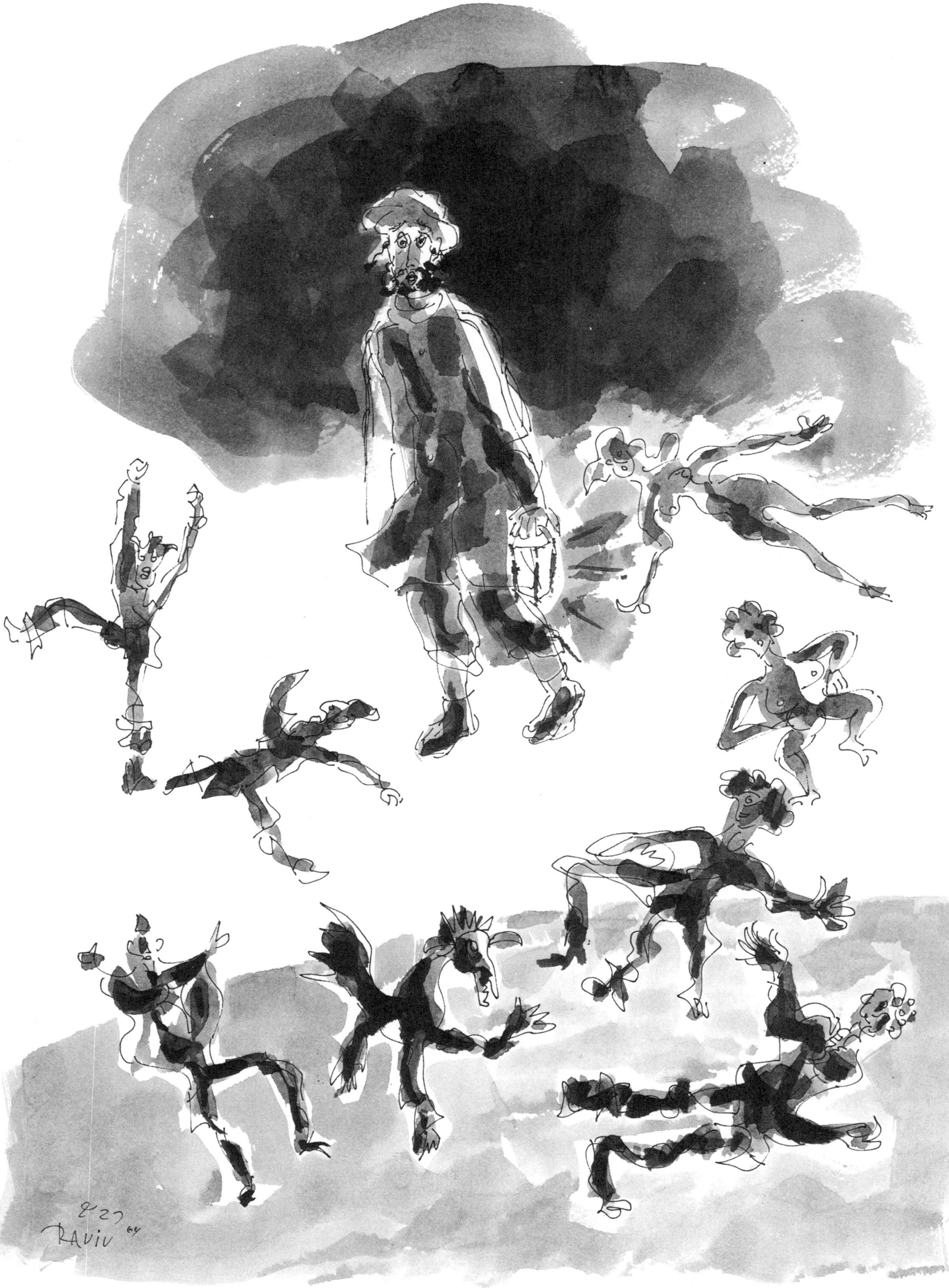
8 27 64
RAVIV

spirit saw me and rose almost to his full height to show me honor. It then began to tremble. I asked it for its name, and it answered so-and-so. I said: "You lie! This is not your name." So it happened thrice and on the fourth time the spirit gave me its true name, even as my Master, of blessed memory, had predicted.

I then whispered into its ear some of the spells. Thereupon the spirit was seized with trembling, and began to rave and wanted to depart. I rebuked it roundly, for it indicated that it wished to leave by way of the small toe and I knew this was a lie. For I saw that it really wanted to depart by way of the throat in order to extinguish the lights and to harm all who were present. Seeing this, I placed a ban upon it and enjoined it from departing. Leaving matters thus, I went for the evening prayer to the house of my Master, of blessed memory. And when we finished our prayers and the disciples left, I repeated to my Master all that had happened. He said to me: "I am surprised at your report. Did I not tell you to go in the *evening?* Why did you then go at night, which is the time when the evil spirits and demons hold sway and none can prevail over them, for this is their time of power. For this reason your effort could not succeed." While he spoke, it grew dark and the rains came down. Then my Master said: "Go in peace and rest the night." And he accompanied me a short distance— which he had never done before, saying: "You must beware of this spirit, seeing that he is greatly angered with you, for you wish to drive him from his place. Now, I want to reveal something to you. But do not be overcome by pride. You see the great power that lies within

you. For many demons fear you and flee before you. Indeed, should all the demons in the world try, they could not do you harm. For when they come, you have only to shake the skirts of your cloak and they will flee from you and not dare to confront you."

Afterwards I wanted to go home by way of the Jewish market place and it was then about one o'clock at night. As I was about to enter the market place, a black dog the size of a donkey sprang at me, and I was so frightened I could not remember a single incantation, for in my fright I forgot everything. And so I walked much distressed and as I came near him, in a narrow lane bordered on both sides by a fence, the night became dark with rain, and I found myself unable to turn back out of fear of the *subashi* and because the demons were behind me and could do me great harm. And when I came near the dog, he emitted a single loud bark, so that I fell to the ground and my hand touched the dog. When I arose, I found the skirts of my cloak to be full of mud, and without any intention to do so I shook them out, and lo and behold!—the dog fled from before me. I then went to my house and found that the hand that had touched the dog was withered.

I came to my Master, of everlasting memory, who said: "Did I not tell you to shake the skirts of your cloak? I even accompanied you and did not enter my house till I saw you safe in yours. And even my thoughts were with you all the time." My Master then took hold of my hand and it was restored to its original state.

Then my Master, of blessed memory, pronounced other spells and I returned to the

house of the woman who was possessed by the spirit. I whispered in her ear but the spirit refused to depart. I returned to my Master, of everlasting memory, and informed him of this. He replied that the spirit was acting in accordance with the command I had given upon it. He then gave me other spells which he wrote out. I went again to the woman, whereupon the spirit began to quake. I then whispered these selfsame spells into her ear. I asked the spirit how it entered the house. It replied: "There was a small hole in the wall and I entered through it, for I could not enter by the door inasmuch as there was affixed to it a proper *mezuza*; nor through the windows which are neither exits nor entrances for human beings and therefore do not require a *mezuza*." I then asked it how it had become embodied in this woman. It answered: "I waited in this house three days until I gained possession of the woman. I waited until she would perform some misdeed, until one Friday morning when she rose up early to begin her work. She struck stone and flint to produce fire. I was sitting on the stone. Strike as she would, no sparks came forth. After much effort without result, she threw the flint *angrily* from her hand. This was my opportunity to enter." I then asked: "What did you do those three days that you were in the house and where did you stay?" It replied: "I hid in one of the branches of a candelabrum. And when the men who were appointed to guard against me came, I hid there and they could not find me." I said: "Give me proof that this is the truth." It replied: "On such-and-such a day you ate such-and-such food; and on such-and-such a day the woman spoke certain

words to her husband who answered her thus-and-so." The couple admitted that this had indeed happened. Then Rabbi Hayim Vital released the spirit from the ban and it departed the body and left the house and by means of the spells of the Master, of everlasting memory, disappeared.

THE incident which is here narrated occurred in Damascus in the time of Rabbi Hayim Vital, of everlasting memory.

Now when the daughter of the beloved and exalted Rabbi Raphael Anaf was still a girl in her father's house, it happened one Friday at twilight that she ate the head of a fish. Straightaway she fainted and was brought to a bed. They covered her face and lit two candles as was their wont each Sabbath eve. Her father and mother and the servants who saw this were taken aback with astonishment. Among those present was Rabbi Jacob Aleman Ashkenazi. And even before the Sabbath had begun, a voice was heard coming from the mouth of the girl and calling Rabbi Raphael to draw near. When he had drawn near, the voice asked: "Why did you prepare just these two candles?" Rabbi Raphael answered that this was his custom every Sabbath. The spirit explained that this Sabbath differed from others and therefore called for more symbols of festivity. He therefore asked Rabbi Raphael to prepare another candle. This was done. The spirit then asked for a chair for Elijah the Prophet, of blessed memory, and another for Rabbi Joseph Karo, of blessed memory, and yet another for

2/27
RAVIV 65

Rabbi Isaac Karo, of blessed memory; altogether seven chairs for seven sages. He then told them to go to the synagogue for the evening prayers and admonished Rabbi Jacob not to reveal anything that he had seen or heard.

When Rabbi Jacob returned home to dress for the Sabbath, his wife asked why he was so late; he replied that he had been discussing business matters with Rabbi Raphael Anaf. But his wife demurred; for it was hardly likely that they would engage in business matters on the Sabbath. She pressed him strongly until he told her that he was delayed because of the evil spirit within a sage which now inhabited the person of Rabbi Raphael's daughter. His wife then queried him thus: "Seeing that he was a sage, why do you call the spirit an evil one?"

When the men were returning from the synagogue, Rabbi Jacob stopped at the house of Rabbi Raphael and called out to him from the doorway. The spirit observed: "This Rabbi Jacob who calls out from the doorway is a fool. I had admonished him not to utter a word and he went and told all to his wife. She has much more understanding than he. For she raised the question as to why he calls the spirit evil, when he is in fact wise." The spirit became angry at Rabbi Jacob and cursed him; whereupon they all entreated the spirit, kissing its hands and feet, until it forgave him.

Rabbi Jacob next hid behind a wine-cask in the store room. The spirit demanded that he be called from there, and spoke derisively: "Look at this man of little sense who thinks I cannot see him behind the casks." The spirit

then asked for a full goblet of wine to recite the *Kiddush*, seated himself on a divan, and recited the *Kiddush* in a loud voice, and all the bystanders sat down to eat. They recited *Birkat Hamazon* and spent a sleepless night watching to see the outcome of this encounter. On the stroke of midnight the spirit called to them and said: "Go to Rabbi Hayim Vital and tell him I want to speak to him." The people replied that they were afraid to be seen by the *subashi*. But even though he told them not to fear for he would accompany them, nevertheless they did not go out. Two hours before sunrise he again told them to go and call Rabbi Hayim Vital because the *subashi* had already left the Jewish quarter. They replied that they were certain the rabbi would not accompany them. He told them to go to the rabbi, whom they would find awake from his sleep, lying on the bed, holding his head in his hands; they should tell him that he had just dreamt a dream and was frightened because he could not remember it. "Let him come to me," said the spirit. "I will recall it to him and explain it." On hearing these words, they went to Rabbi Hayim Vital, of everlasting memory, and found him exactly as the spirit had foretold. When they delivered the spirit's message, he dressed and came to it. As they greeted each other, the spirit showed him great honor.

The spirit then said: "In the dream that you had, a man sent you seven sages together with a sick person whom you should heal. This is the dream you forgot and this is its meaning. The man who sent the seven sages is your master, the Ari. The seven sages are

Elijah, Rabbi Joseph Karo, Rabbi Isaac Karo, and four others, all of blessed memory. The sick one was my own self and your Master asked me to give you his greetings and also instructions to do certain things and be sure not to forget them. And I myself eagerly look forward to your healing me. In order to discharge my obligations to you in full, I shall disclose to you now the entire matter. Know that I am so-and-so who once lived in Safed (may it be firmly established in our day). Forty years ago my soul left its mortal coil. During these forty years I was raised from one level of hell to another and in each ascension I was given due punishment for my remaining sins.

"Finally, when I was to be judged at a special level, my lightest misdeeds were given the most rigorous scrutiny. I was not allowed to enter a new level because I was found to have committed some minor sin. And while I was at that transitory stage very near a level, I heard behind the veil of the Heavenly Court a voice which called out: 'Whom shall we send and who will go for us to make known to the Jews of Damascus that because of their sins and transgressions a plague had been decreed upon them? There is need that they be informed of this so that they may repent and set aright their misdeeds and thereby annul this decree.' On hearing this, I cried out: 'Here am I; send me.' I was told to go and relate all I had heard, and in carrying out this mission, I would also erase my own sins and on my return would be able to enter my own level.

"I sought a means to enter upon this earth and found it by way of the river Euphrates in the city of Bozrah which is near Damascus. I came into the body of a fish which was then caught by a fisherman. Thereupon I prayed to His Blessed Name that I should not fall into the hands of gentiles but into those of Jews. The fisherman brought me and the other fish to your market. Even then I yet prayed to His Blessed Name that I fall into the hands of a worthy Jew. Now as evening drew nigh, Solomon Hagavil came to buy me and I prayed not to be delivered into the hands of such an evil man, and His Blessed Name heard my entreaty and spared me. For there came the honorable and worthy Rabbi Raphael who took me and brought me to his house and told his wife to hasten and prepare for the Sabbath. On finding matters thus, I was happy. But when the fish was being scaled, I suffered great pain and retreated to the head of the fish. When the fish was cooked, this young girl came and ate a portion from the head. And as I was hidden there, I could enter into this girl. For she was pure, a spark emanating from Queen Esther."

After his tale was ended, the spirit told Rabbi Hayim Vital: "Go to your prayers and immediately thereafter come to me. I will then reveal to you such hidden things as you never before heard from your Master. Also admonish the people to repent, to give charity, and to fast." Rabbi Hayim then asked: "Who are they who are worthy to join me on this mission?" The spirit replied: "The sages: Rabbi Jacob Abulafia, who is now in Safed, and Rabbi Hosea Pinto; and also call upon Rabbi Joseph Mataron, who is without blemish." Rabbi Hayim asked: "Shall I also call the sage Rabbi Israel Nejara?" The spirit emphatically re-

plied: "Do not invite that shameful man. For even though his songs cheer God and man, and are held in favor by God, nevertheless he is a base fellow. For he eats at the Lord's table in an uncovered head with only a red band around it, and with bared arms, in the company of nude men, and they all eat and drink together, and he pays no heed to their nudity."

Hearing these things, Rabbi Hayim then went to his prayers, left the synagogue, ate his meal at home, but did not return to the spirit. At the time of the *Minchah* prayer, some people wanted to go and call him but they were restrained by the spirit, who said: "It should be clear to you that the saga Rabbi Hayim Vital is conducting himself haughtily toward me. For he is waiting until I call him. Now I have already told him to come to me immediately after his prayers and have already explained my entire mission to him. Thus I have discharged my obligation and he is the loser in that I can no longer reveal secret things to him since I am now departing for my next level."

During the *Minchah* service a learned man in the synagogue of the Sephardim gave a discourse. The spirit derided him. "Look at this preacher who rebukes his listeners for their sins, while he is himself full of sins." When the time for reciting the *Havdalah* came, the spirit said: "Recite the *Havdalah*, because the time has come for me to leave here for my own level." And it also said: "When the dawn comes, the sage, Rabbi Hayim Vital, will come to speak to me. Tell him that today being the Sabbath I had the right to reveal to him hidden secrets which he had not yet heard.

I have already told him this, but he has not come." The *Havdalah* was recited and the spirit became silent. In the morning Rabbi Hayim Vital arrived and was told all that the spirit had said. Rabbi Hayim did not say a word to it. He called to Joshua Albo, who came before him, and he gave him an incantation whereby the spirit would be prevailed upon to leave by way of the small toe of the girl.

After the spirit had departed, the girl began to speak foolishly. Meantime the sage Rabbi Jacob Abulafia arrived from Safed and on hearing these things went to speak to the spirit but concluded that matters were not as they should be. He told this to Rabbi Hayim Vital and added: "The original spirit was that of a great sage and was holy and spoke only the truth. However, it has already departed and gone hence. And as for the foolish prattle of the girl at this time—it is because wherever holiness abides, it leaves its imprint, and defilement seeks eagerly to cleave there. Therefore, when this holy spirit left her, at once a spark from the devil's abode came into her. Thus her words have no reality."

And when the evil spirit departed from the girl she became once again pure and wholesome as before.

SOME days later it happened that Rabbi Hayim Vital, of blessed memory, asked the Ari, of blessed memory, the meaning of an obscure passage in the Tosefta. The Ari pleaded with Rabbi Hayim: "As you love life itself,

I urge you not to press me for an explanation. It will be better for you and me and the whole world. For this holds within it a deep hidden meaning which the Heavenly Powers do not want me to explain." Rabbi Hayim insisted: "You must reveal it to me." Once again the Ari said: "If I reveal this to you, you will regret it greatly. I have great fears for you. Nevertheless it is required of me not to hold back from you whatever you ask. I therefore beg of you not to persist that I reveal the meaning of this passage from the Tosefta to you." Rabbi Hayim replied: "But I insist that you give this meaning." Reluctantly the Ari yielded to him and revealed its meaning. He then said to Rabbi Hayim: "The decree has been proclaimed that the Ari shall die within this year, because I made known to you this secret. You have of your own doing brought upon you this calamity. For had you not been so persistent, I would not have made the revelation to you, and would have been spared punishment by Heaven. I put this to you ever so many times but you would not heed my words. Now I have no concern for myself or my family. But I do feel sorry for you, my disciples. For how can I part from you without your having attained perfection?" — As for this secret, we have not yet been worthy of it. It remains hidden with Rabbi Hayim Vital, who cannot reveal it until such time as the Holy One, Blessed Be He, has designated. — On hearing this, the disciples were sadly distressed and said: "Would that we had not asked for this revelation!"

After this incident the Ari built a compound for these ten disciples and in its courtyard set up separate rooms for the women and children. At the end of the fifth month a quarrel broke out among the wives on the Sabbath eve and they told their husbands about it. Eventually the husbands became involved in the dispute. Now the Master, of everlasting memory, had always urged upon them to dwell together in love and harmony and peace. But on this day, prompted by a wayward impulse, they disregarded his admonitions. And toward evening the Master went with the disciples outside the city limits and then returned to the synagogue downcast and sad and sat dejectedly throughout the prayers. When Rabbi Hayim Vital saw him in this state, which was very unlike him, he was startled. At the close of the prayers, Rabbi Hayim Vital approached him, saying: "Master, why did you appear so downcast and bitter of soul during the prayers?" The Master replied: "Because I saw the angel of death when I went to greet the Sabbath, and he recited this verse: (I Samuel, 12): 'Both you and your King shall perish.' " From this it would seem that his final decree had been sealed. And this was as a result of the quarrel among the disciples. For as long as peace prevailed, the Adversary was powerless. And so it was that in that very year our Master and teacher, the crown of our head, together with five of the disciples, was summoned to the Higher Court and the light of Israel was dimmed.

Before his death, the Master cautioned Rabbi Isaac Sagis to tell the disciples to beware of studying the esoteric lore, as they were not yet fully ready for it. For if they did, their lives might, God forbid, be cut short. How-

ever, should the generation prove worthy, he would come back and teach them. On hearing this, they asked: "How can this be? For when our Master returns, we shall be old and he a mere lad, and how can we learn from him?" He answered: "It will come to pass whether it be in a dream or while awake or by whatsoever way it may be."

And when his soul was about to expire, Rabbi Joseph Hakohen was with him. The Master told him that were this generation worthy, then this very year would have been the year of redemption and of the true Messianic age. Then the Master sadly added, quoting Genesis 38: "And she yet again bore a son and called his name Shela; and she was at Chezib (a place name whose root meaning alludes to frustrated hope) when she bore him." He then said to him: "Leave quickly, for you are a *Kohen* and I am at death's door." And as soon as Rabbi Joseph Hakohen left, the Master's soul was taken from him with a divine kiss.

After his death the disciples gathered to perform on his body the ritual immersion. As they placed him in the water they asked his forgiveness so that they might wash his body. Thereupon he bent his head and performed the rite of immersion upon himself.

The text of this book was set in Century Expanded type by Graphic Arts Composition, Inc., of Philadelphia and lithographed by General Offset Co., Inc., of New York City. It was bound by Publishers Book Bindery, Inc., of Long Island City, New York.